JOHN THOMPSON'S
EASIEST PIANO COURSE

FIRST CHART TOPPERS

This collection of popular piano songs is intended as supplementary material for those working through **John Thompson's Easiest Piano Course** Parts 2–4. The pieces may also be used for sight reading practice by more advanced students.

Dynamics and phrasing have been deliberately omitted from the earlier pieces, since they are not introduced until Part 3 of the Easiest Piano Course, and initially the student's attention should be focused on playing notes and rhythms accurately. Outline fingering has been included, and in general the hand is assumed to remain in a five-finger position until a new fingering indicates a position shift. The fingering should suit most hands, although logical alternatives are always possible.

Counting Stars

Words & Music by Ryan Tedder

Lately I been, I been los-ing sleep, dream-ing a-bout the things that

we could be. Ba - by, I been, I been pray-in' hard;

said no more count-ing dol-lars, we'll be count-ing stars. Late-ly I been,

2

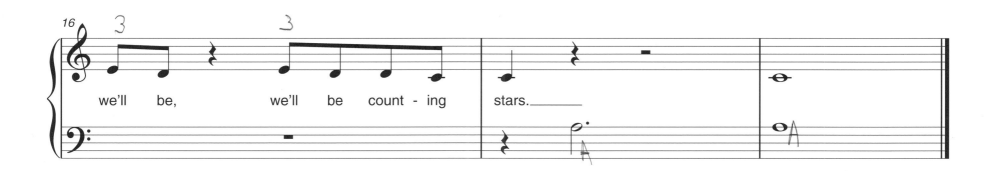

Let Her Go

Words & Music by Michael Rosenberg

Simply

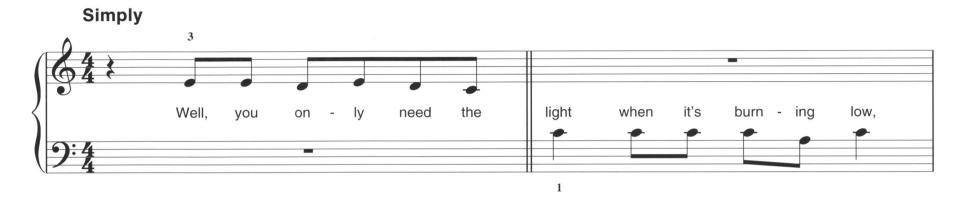

Well, you on - ly need the light when it's burn - ing low,

on - ly miss the sun when it starts to snow,__ on - ly know you

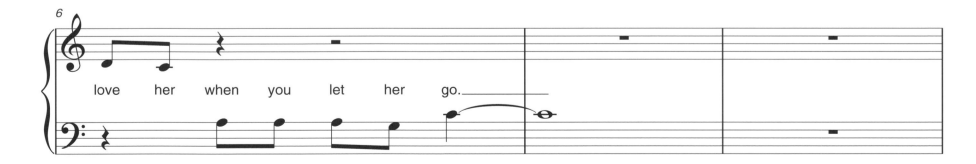

love her when you let her go.__

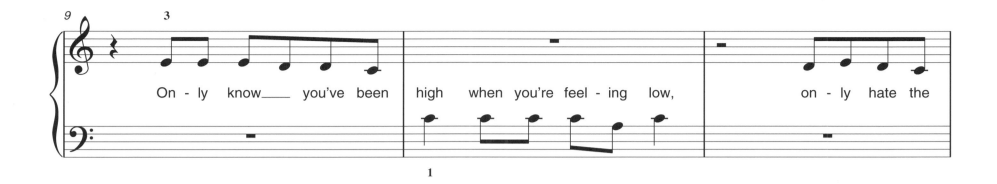

On - ly know____ you've been high when you're feel - ing low, on - ly hate the

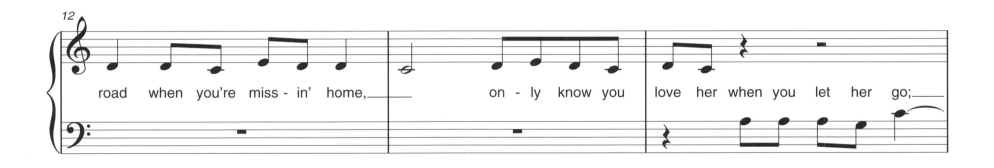

road when you're miss - in' home,____ on - ly know you love her when you let her go;____

and you let her go.____

I Knew You Were Trouble

Words & Music by Max Martin, Taylor Swift & Shellback

Confidently

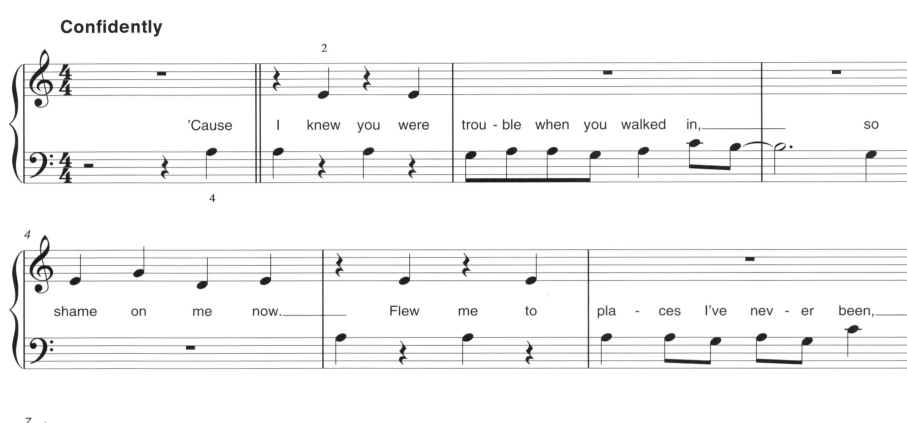

7

Wake Me Up

Words & Music by Aloe Blacc, Tim Bergling & Michael Einziger

Lightly, with a bounce

Right Place Right Time

Words & Music by Stephen Robson, Claude Kelly & Oliver Murs

Rhythmically

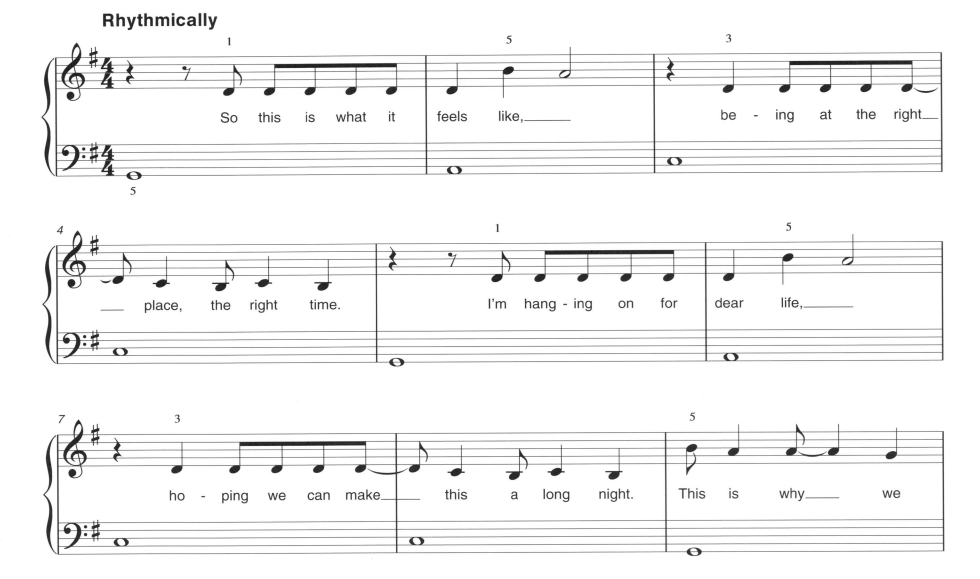

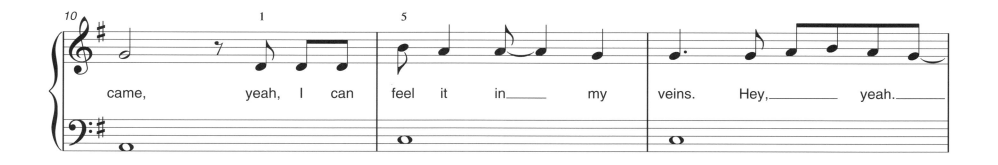

came,   yeah, I can   feel it in____ my   veins. Hey,_____ yeah.____

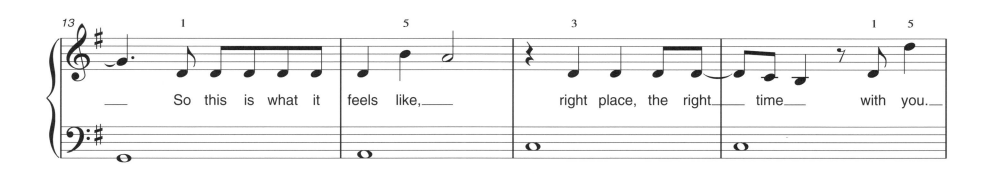

____ So this is what it   feels like,____   right place, the right____ time____ with you.____

The right place, the right____ time.____

Happy

Words & Music by Pharrell Williams

12

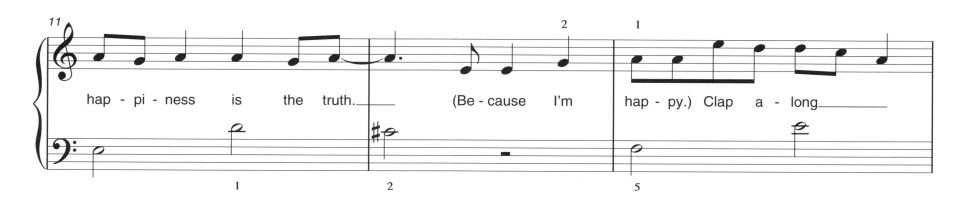

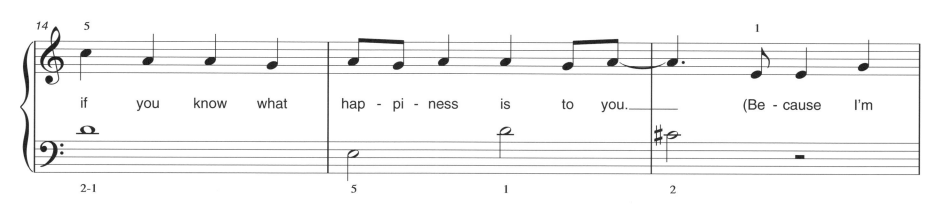

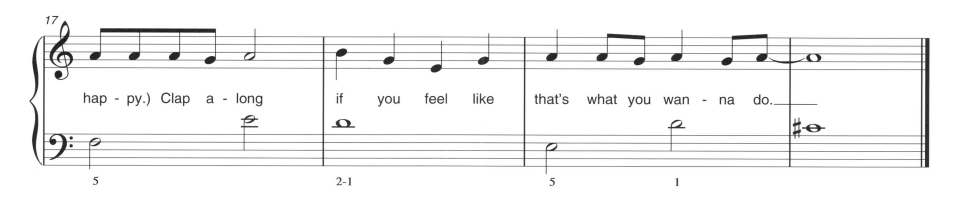

All Of Me

Words & Music by John Legend & Tobias Gad

Passionately

you're my end and my be - gin - ning, e - ven when I lose, I'm win -

- ning. 'Cause I give you all of me.

And you give me all of you, oh.

Say Something

Words & Music by Mike Campbell, Chad Vaccarino & Ian Axel

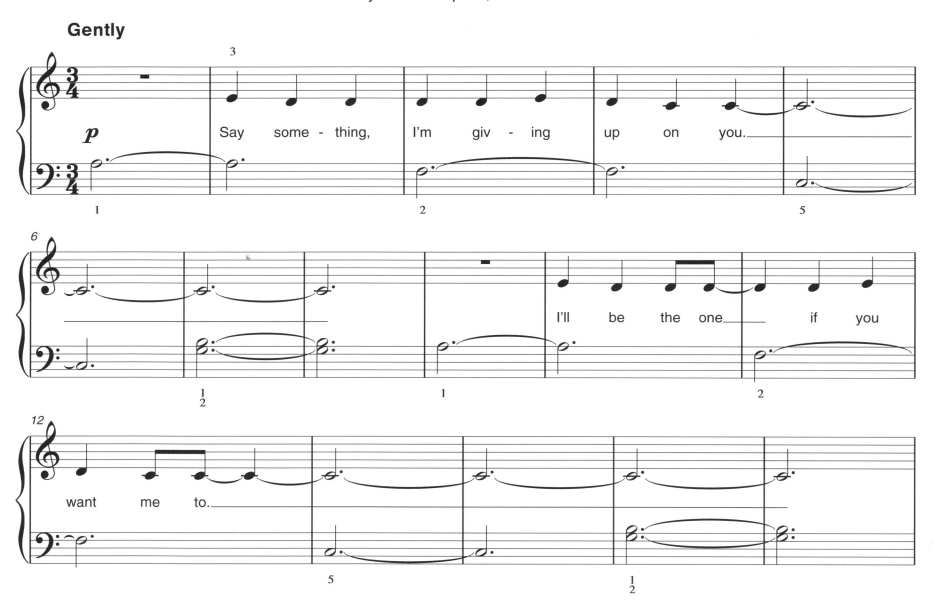

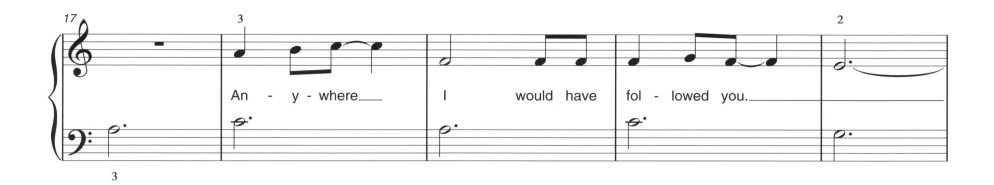

An - y - where___   I   would have   fol - lowed you.___

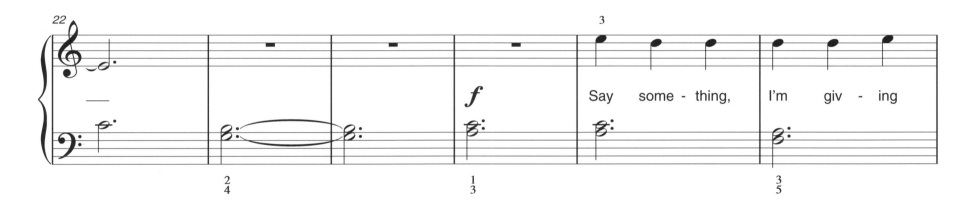

___   *f*   Say   some - thing,   I'm   giv - ing

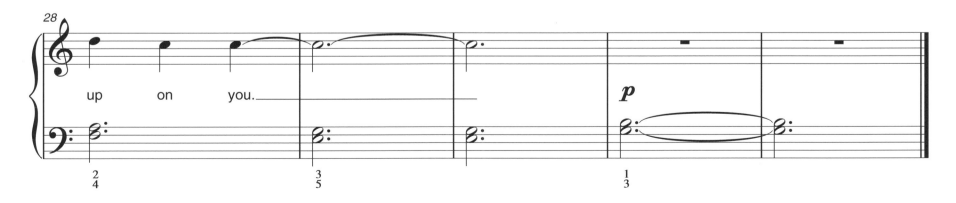

up   on   you.___   *p*

A Sky Full Of Stars

Words & Music by Guy Berryman, Jonathan Buckland, William Champion, Christopher Martin & Tim Bergling

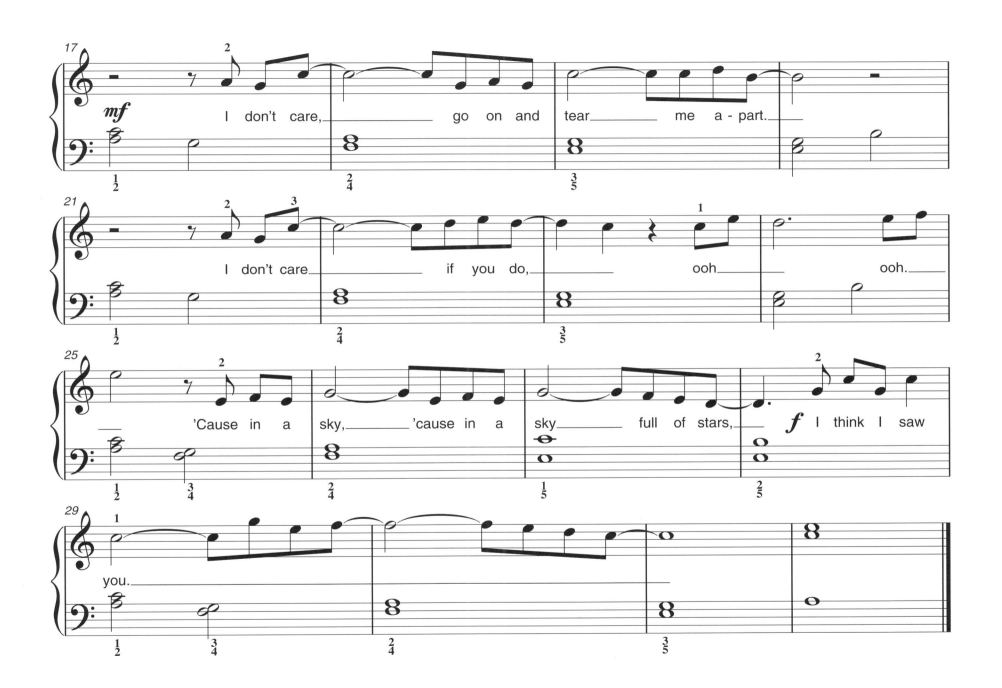

Call My Name

Words & Music by Calvin Harris

Energetically

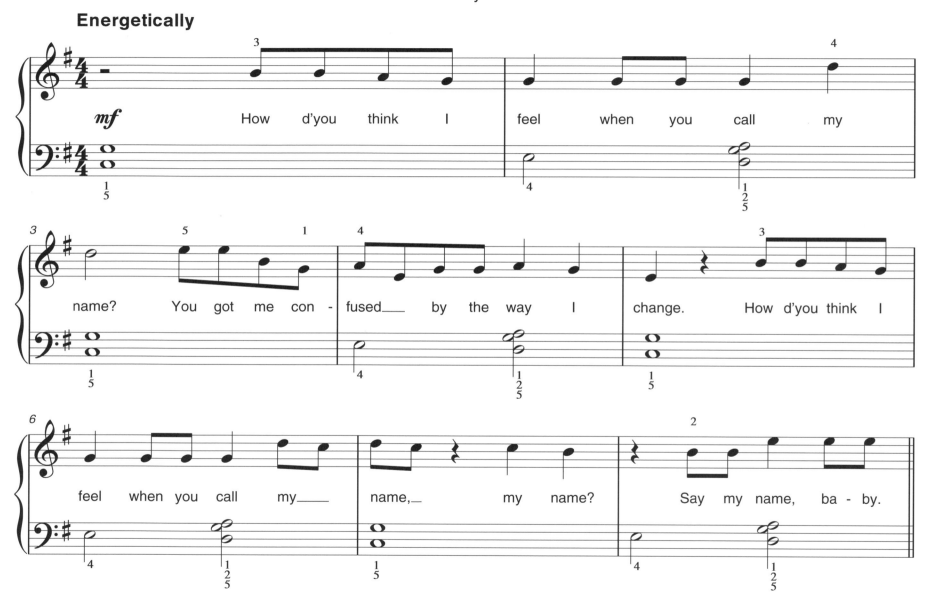

How d'you think I feel when you call my name? You got me con-

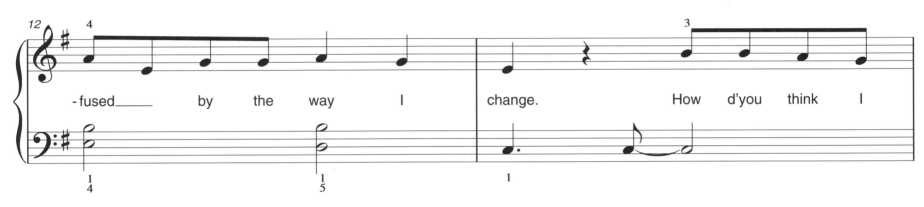

-fused_____ by the way I change. How d'you think I

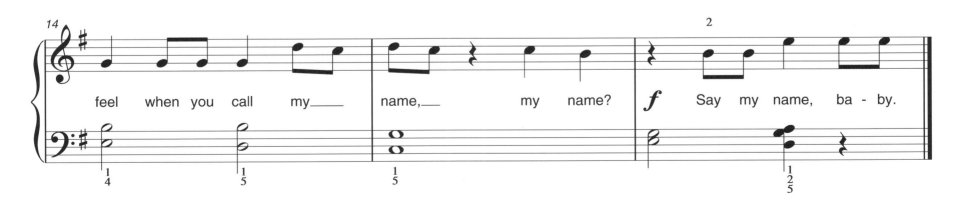

feel when you call my_____ name,_____ my name? *f* Say my name, ba - by.

Roar

Words & Music by Katy Perry, Lukasz Gottwald, Bonnie McKee, Martin Max & Henry Russell Walter

Heavily

Photograph

Words & Music by Ed Sheeran & John McDaid

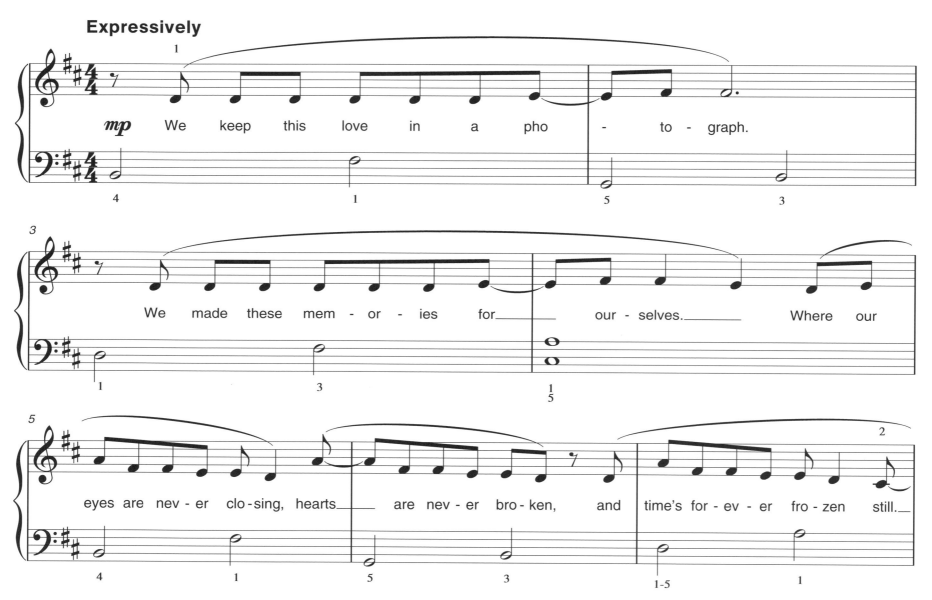

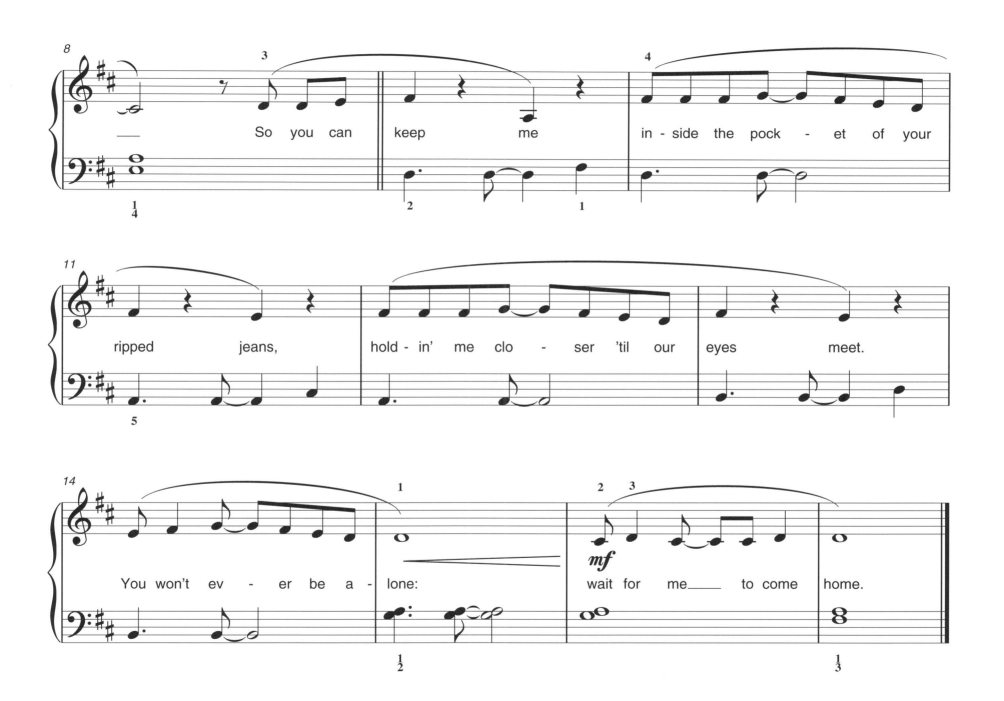

What Makes You Beautiful

Words & Music by Savan Kotecha, Carl Falk & Rami Yacoub

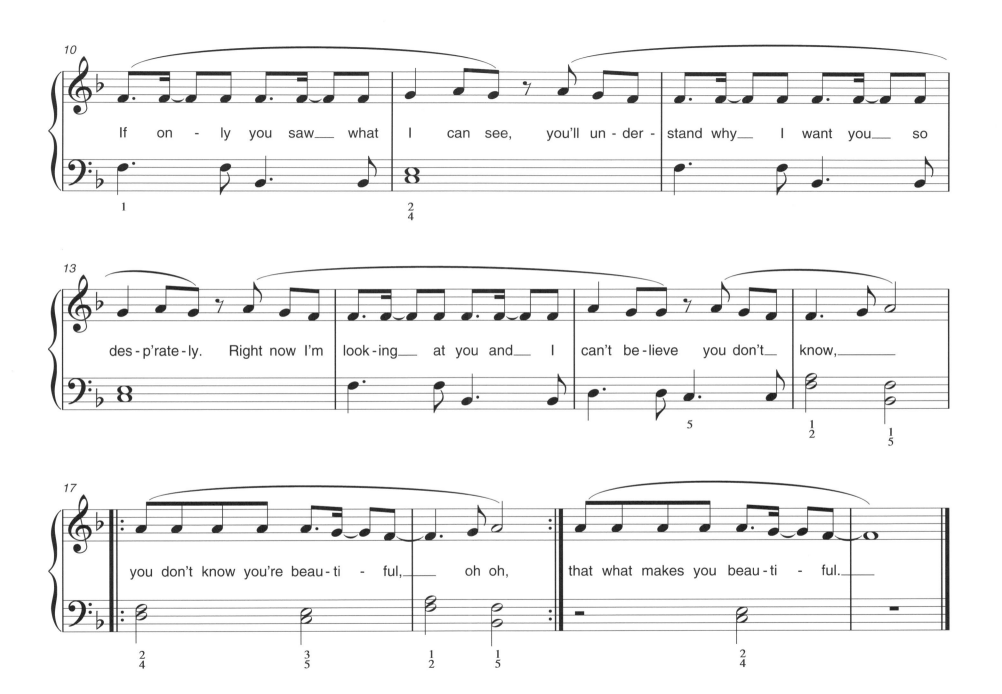

Pompeii

Words & Music by Daniel Campbell Smith

Best Song Ever

Words & Music by Wayne Hector, John Ryan, Julian Bunetta & Edward Drewett

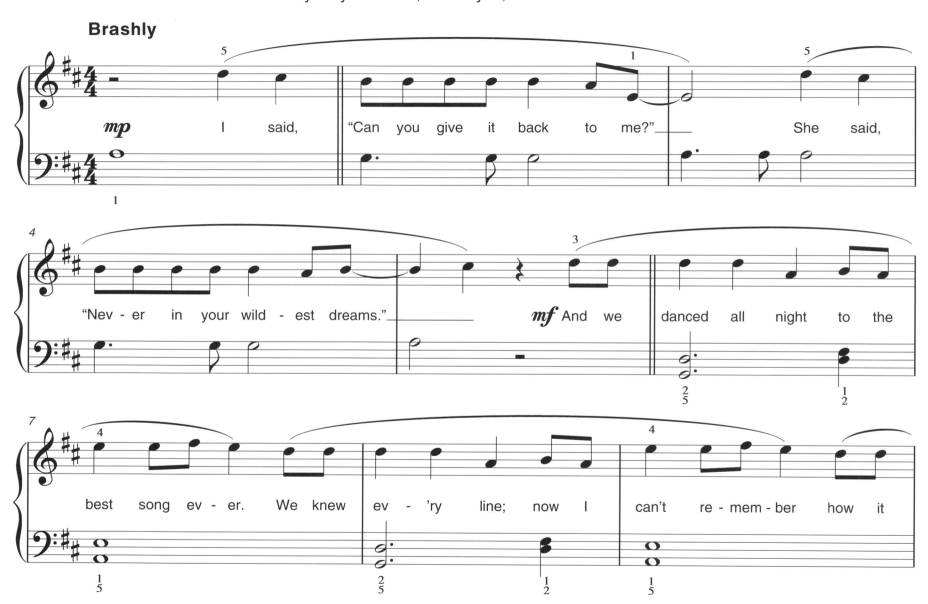

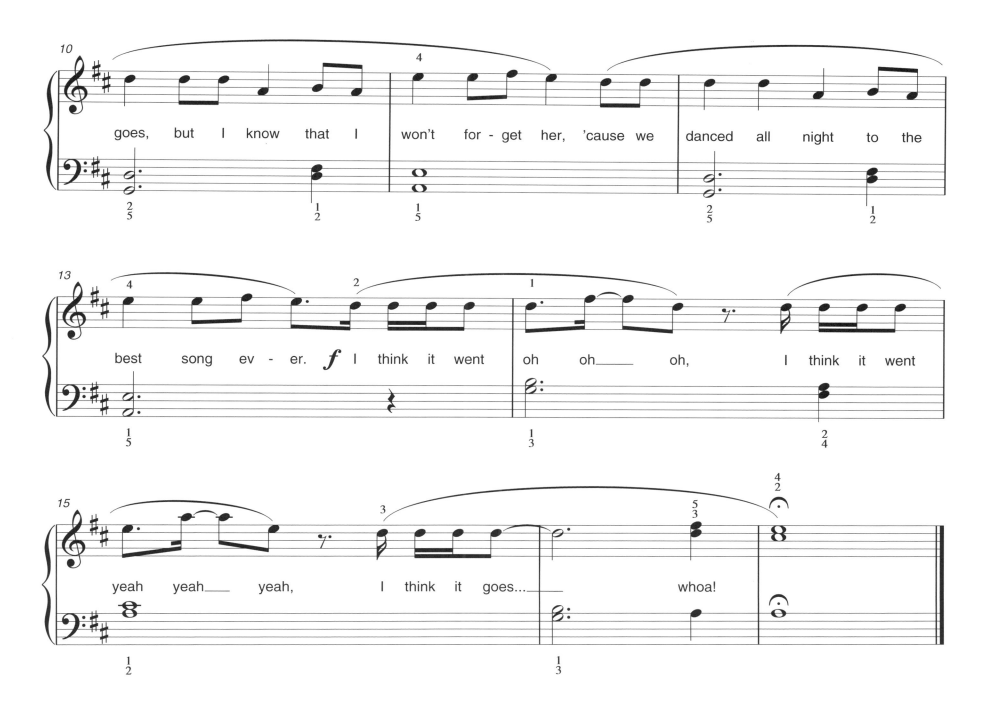

goes, but I know that I won't for - get her, 'cause we danced all night to the

best song ev - er. *f* I think it went oh oh___ oh, I think it went

yeah yeah___ yeah, I think it goes... whoa!

Exclusive Distributors:
Music Sales Limited
Newmarket Road, Bury St Edmunds, Suffolk IP33 3YB, UK.
Music Sales Pty Limited
Units 3-4, 17 Willfox Street, Condell Park, NSW 2200, Australia.

Order No. WMR101497
ISBN: 978-1-78305-653-8

Arranged by Christopher Hussey.
Arrangements and engravings supplied by Camden Music Services.
Edited by Sam Lung.

Printed in the EU.